PRENTICE HALL MATHEMATICS
ALGEBRA 1

Chapter 1
Support File

Tools of Algebra

Prentice
Hall

Needham, Massachusetts
Upper Saddle River, New Jersey
Glenview, Illinois

ISBN: 0-13-063806-4

1 2 3 4 5 6 7 8 9 10   06 05 04 03 02

Chapter 1

Tools of Algebra

Practice 1-1

Write an algebraic expression for each phrase.

1. 7 increased by x

2. p multiplied by 3

3. 10 decreased by m

4. n less than 7

5. the product of 2 and q

6. 3 more than m

Write a phrase for each algebraic expression.

7. $\frac{8}{a}$

8. $s - 10$

9. $x + 13$

10. $ab + 2$

Define a variable and write an algebraic expression for each phrase.

11. the difference of 8 and a number

12. the sum of 4 and a number

13. the product of 2 and a number

14. 3 increased by a number

15. 10 plus the quotient of a number and 15

16. 12 less than a number

Define a variable and write an algebraic equation to model each situation.

17. What is the total cost of buying several shirts at $24.95 each?

18. The number of gal of water used to water trees is 30 times the number of trees.

19. What is the amount of money in a bank containing only dimes?

20. What is the number of marbles left in a 48-marble bag after some marbles have been given away?

21. The total cost equals the price of the tickets multiplied by eight people.

22. What is the cost of buying several pairs of pants at $32.95 per pair?

Write an equation to model the relationship in each table.

23.

Number of Tickets	Total Cost
2	$7
4	$14
6	$21

24.

Number of Hours	Distance Traveled
1	55 mi
3	165 mi
5	275 mi

25.

Number of Hours	Total Pay
8	$40
12	$60
16	$80

26.

Total Cost	Change from $10
$10.00	$0
$9.00	$1.00
$7.50	$2.50

27.

Number of Days	Length
1	0.45 in.
4	1.80 in.
8	3.60 in.

28.

Miles Traveled	Miles Remaining
0	500
125	375
350	150

Practice 1-2

Simplify each expression.

1. $4 + 6(8)$

2. $\dfrac{4(8-2)}{3+9}$

3. $4 \times 3^2 + 2$

4. $40 \div 5(2)$

5. $2.7 + 3.6 \times 4.5$

6. $3[4(8-2)+5]$

7. $4 + 3(15 - 2^3)$

8. $17 - [(3+2) \times 2]$

9. $6 \times (3+2) \div 15$

Evaluate each expression.

10. $\dfrac{a+2b}{5}$ for $a = 1$ and $b = 2$

11. $\dfrac{5m+n}{5}$ for $m = 6$ and $n = 15$

12. $x + 3y^2$ for $x = 3.4$ and $y = 3$

13. $7a - 4(b+2)$ for $a = 5$ and $b = 2$

Simplify each expression.

14. $\dfrac{100-15}{9+8}$

15. $\dfrac{2(3+4)}{7}$

16. $\dfrac{3(4+12)}{2(7-3)}$

17. $14 + 3 \times 4$

18. $8 + 3(4+3)$

19. $3 + 4[13 - 2(6-3)]$

20. $8(5 + 30 \div 5)$

21. $(3.4)(2.7) + 5$

22. $50 \div 2 + 15 \times 4$

23. $7(9-5)$

24. $2(3^2) - 3(2)$

25. $4 + 8 \div 2 + 6 \times 3$

26. $(7+8) \div (4-1)$

27. $5[2(8+5)-15]$

28. $(6+8) \times (8-4)$

29. $12\left(\dfrac{6+30}{9-3}\right)$

30. $14 + 6 \times 2^3 - 8 \div 2^2$

31. $\dfrac{7(14)-3(6)}{2}$

32. $14 \div [3(8-2)-11]$

33. $3\left(\dfrac{9+13}{6}\right)$

34. $\dfrac{4(8-3)}{3+2}$

35. $5 + 4^2 \times 8 - 2^3 \div 2^2$

36. $4^2 + 5^2(8-3)$

37. $5(3^2+2) - 2(6^2 - 5^2)$

Evaluate each expression for $a = 2$ and $b = 6$.

38. $2(7a - b)$

39. $(a^3 + b^2) \div a$

40. $3b \div (2a - 1) + b$

41. $\dfrac{5a+2}{b}$

42. $\dfrac{3(b-2)}{4(a+1)}$

43. $9b + a^4 \div 8$

Use the expression $r + 0.12m$ to calculate the cost of renting a car. The basic rate is r. The number of miles driven is m.

44. The basic rate is \$15.95. The car is driven 150 mi.

45. The basic rate is \$32.50. The car is driven 257 mi.

Evaluate each expression for $s = 3$ and $t = 9$.

46. $8(4s - t)$

47. $(2t - 3s) \div 4$

48. $t^2 - s^4$

49. $s(3t + 6)$

50. $\dfrac{5s^2}{t}$

51. $\dfrac{2t^2}{s^3}$

Practice 1-3

Name the set(s) of numbers to which each number belongs.

1. -0.002

2. $12\frac{1}{2}$

3. 8

4. 5π

5. $\sqrt{7}$

6. -22

7. -3.4

8. $\sqrt{36}$

Decide whether each statement is *true* or *false*. If the statement is false, give a counterexample.

9. Every whole number is an integer.

10. Every integer is a whole number.

11. Every rational number is a real number.

12. Every multiple of 7 is odd.

Use <, =, or > to compare.

13. $-10.98 \ \blacksquare \ -10.99$

14. $-\frac{1}{3} \ \blacksquare \ -0.3$

15. $-\frac{11}{5} \ \blacksquare \ -\frac{4}{5}$

16. $-\frac{1}{2} \ \blacksquare \ -\frac{5}{10}$

17. $-\frac{3}{8} \ \blacksquare \ -\frac{7}{16}$

18. $\frac{3}{4} \ \blacksquare \ \frac{13}{16}$

Write in order from least to greatest.

19. $-\frac{8}{9}, -\frac{7}{8}, -\frac{22}{25}$

20. $-3\frac{4}{9}, -3.45, -3\frac{12}{25}$

21. $-\frac{1}{4}, -\frac{1}{5}, -\frac{1}{3}$

22. $-1.7, -1\frac{3}{4}, -1\frac{7}{9}$

23. $-\frac{3}{4}, -\frac{7}{8}, -\frac{2}{3}$

24. $2\frac{3}{4}, 2\frac{5}{8}, 2.7$

Determine which set of numbers is most reasonable for each situation.

25. the number of dolphins in the ocean

26. the height of a basketball player

27. the number of pets you have

28. the circumference of a compact disk

Find each absolute value.

29. $\left|\frac{3}{10}\right|$

30. $|-327|$

31. $|-3.46|$

32. $\left|-\frac{1}{2}\right|$

33. Name the sets(s) of numbers to which each number in the table belongs. Choose among: whole numbers, integers, rational numbers, irrational numbers, and real numbers.

Type of Account	Principal	Rate	Time (years)	Interest
Checking	$154.23	0.0375	$\frac{30}{365}$	$.48
Savings	$8000	0.055	$3\frac{1}{2}$	$1540

Practice 1-4

Adding Real Numbers

Simplify each expression.

1. $6 + (-4)$

2. $-2 + (-13)$

3. $-18 + 4$

4. $15 + (-32)$

5. $-27 + (-14)$

6. $8 + (-3)$

7. $-12.2 + 31.9$

8. $-2.3 + (-13.9)$

9. $19.8 + (-27.4)$

10. $\frac{1}{4} + \left(-\frac{3}{4}\right)$

11. $\frac{2}{3} + \left(-\frac{1}{3}\right)$

12. $-\frac{7}{12} + \frac{1}{6}$

13. $2\frac{2}{3} + (-1)$

14. $-3\frac{3}{4} + 1\frac{1}{2}$

15. $2\frac{1}{3} + \left(-4\frac{2}{3}\right)$

16. $-6.3 + 8.2$

17. $-3.82 + 2.83$

18. $-7.8 + 9$

19. $|-12| + |-21|$

20. $|-13 + 6|$

21. $-14 + |-7|$

Evaluate each expression for $m = 2.5$.

22. $-m + 1.6$

23. $-3.2 + m$

24. $-2.5 + (-m)$

Simplify.

25. $-3 + (-6) + 14$

26. $4 + (-8) + (-14)$

27. $2.7 + (-3.2) + 1.5$

28. $-2.5 + (-1.2) + (-2.3)$

29. $\frac{1}{2} + \left(-\frac{1}{3}\right) + \frac{1}{4}$

30. $-\frac{2}{3} + \left(-\frac{1}{3}\right) + \left(-1\frac{1}{3}\right)$

Simplify.

31. $\begin{bmatrix} 4 & -1 \\ 2 & 5 \end{bmatrix} + \begin{bmatrix} -1 & 2 \\ -2 & -3 \end{bmatrix}$

32. $\begin{bmatrix} -4.7 \\ 2.3 \\ -1.5 \end{bmatrix} + \begin{bmatrix} 5.1 \\ -2.7 \\ 2.6 \end{bmatrix}$

33. The temperature at 5:00 A.M. is $-38°F$. The temperature rises 20° by 11:00 A.M. What is the temperature at 11:00 A.M.?

34. A football team has possession of the ball on their own 15-yd line. The next two plays result in a loss of 7 yd and a gain of 3 yd, respectively. On what yard line is the ball after the two plays?

35. Suppose your opening checking account balance is $124.53. After you write a check for $57.49 and make a deposit of $103.49, what is your new balance?

36. During an emergency exercise, a submarine dives 37 ft, rises 16 ft, and then dives 18 ft. What is the net change in the submarine's position after the second dive?

Practice 1-5

Simplify.

1. $13 - 6$ **2.** $19 - 35$ **3.** $-4 - 8$

4. $-14 - (-6)$ **5.** $18 - (-25)$ **6.** $-32 - 17$

7. $-6.8 - 14.6$ **8.** $-9.3 - (-23.9)$ **9.** $-8.2 - 0.8$

10. $18.3 - (-8.1)$ **11.** $-3 - (-15)$ **12.** $6.4 - 17$

13. $\frac{3}{4} - 1\frac{1}{4}$ **14.** $-\frac{1}{3} - \frac{2}{3}$ **15.** $-\frac{1}{4} - \left(-\frac{3}{4}\right)$

16. $|-11| - |-29|$ **17.** $|-4 - 8|$ **18.** $|9.8| - |-15.7|$

19. $|-8 - (-32)|$ **20.** $|3.7 - (-6.8)|$ **21.** $2.83 - 3.82$

Evaluate each expression for $c = -3$ and $d = -6$.

22. $c - d$ **23.** $-c - d$ **24.** $-c - (-d)$

25. $|c + d|$ **26.** $-c + d$ **27.** $3c - 2d$

Simplify.

28. $8 - (-4) - (-5)$ **29.** $6 - 10 - 4$ **30.** $10 - 14 - 15$

31. $-6 - 3 - (-2)$ **32.** $-5 + 7 - 9$ **33.** $-2 - 2 - 4$

Subtract.

34. $\begin{bmatrix} -3 & -1 \\ 2 & 4 \end{bmatrix} - \begin{bmatrix} 5 & -2 \\ -3 & 8 \end{bmatrix}$ **35.** $\begin{bmatrix} 6.1 & -4 \\ -3.7 & -2.1 \end{bmatrix} - \begin{bmatrix} 7.0 & -2.3 \\ -1.6 & 4.2 \end{bmatrix}$

36. The temperature in the evening was 68°F. The following morning, the temperature was 39°F. What is the difference between the two temperatures?

37. What is the difference in altitude between Mt. Everest, which is about 29,028 ft above sea level, and Death Valley, which is about 282 ft below sea level?

38. Suppose the balance in your checking account was $234.15 when you wrote a check for $439.87. (This is known as overdrawing your account.) Describe the account's new balance.

39. After three plays in which a football team lost 7 yd, gained 3 yd, and lost 1 yd, respectively, the ball was placed on the team's own 30-yd line. Where was the ball before the three plays?

Practice 1-6

Multiplying and Dividing Real Numbers

Simplify each expression.

1. $(-2)(8)$

2. $(-6)(-9)$

3. $(-3)^4$

4. -2^5

5. $(6)(-8)$

6. $(-14)^2$

7. $2(-4)(-6)$

8. $-30 \div (-5)$

9. $\frac{-52}{-13}$

10. $(-8)(5)(-3)$

11. -7^2

12. -3^5

13. $\frac{-68}{17}$

14. $\frac{(-4)(-13)}{-26}$

15. $\frac{225}{(-3)(-5)}$

Evaluate each expression.

16. x^3 for $x = -5$

17. $s^2 t \div 10$ for $s = -2$ and $t = 10$

18. $-2m + 4n^2$ for $m = -6$ and $n = -5$

19. $\frac{v}{w}$ for $v = \frac{2}{5}$ and $w = -\frac{1}{2}$

20. $-cd^2$ for $c = 2$ and $d = -4$

21. $(x + 4)^2$ for $x = -11$

22. $\left(\frac{a}{b}\right)^2 + b^3$ for $a = 24$ and $b = -6$

23. $4p^2 + 7q^3$ for $p = -3$ and $q = -2$

24. $(e + f)^4$ for $e = -3$ and $f = 7$

25. $5f^2 - z^2$ for $f = -1$ and $z = -4$

Simplify each expression.

26. $2^4 - 3^2 + 5^2$

27. $(-8)^2 - 4^3$

28. $32 \div (-7 + 5)^3$

29. $\frac{3}{4} \div \left(-\frac{3}{7}\right)$

30. $18 + 4^2 \div (-8)$

31. $26 \div [4 - (-9)]$

32. $4^3 - (2 - 5)^3$

33. $-(-4)^3$

34. $(-8)(-5)(-3)$

35. $(-3)^2 - 4^2$

36. $\frac{-45}{-15}$

37. $(-2)^6$

38. $\frac{-90}{6}$

39. $\frac{-15}{(7 - 4)}$

40. $\frac{195}{-13}$

Evaluate each expression.

41. $(a + b)^2$ for $a = 6$ and $b = -8$

42. $d^3 \div e$ for $d = -6$ and $e = -3$

43. $(m + 5n)^3$ for $m = 2$ and $n = -1$

44. $j^5 - 5k$ for $j = -4$ and $k = -1$

45. $xy + z$ for $x = -4, y = 3$, and $z = -3$

46. $4s \div (-3t)$ for $s = -6$ and $t = -2$

47. $\frac{r^3}{s}$ for $r = -6$ and $s = -2$

48. $\frac{-h^5}{-4}$ for $h = 4$

Practice 1-7

The Distributive Property

Simplify each expression.

1. $2(x + 6)$

2. $-5(8 - b)$

3. $4(-x + 7)$

4. $(5c - 7)(-3)$

5. $-2.5(3a + 5)$

6. $-(3k - 12)$

7. $-\frac{3}{4}(12 - 16d)$

8. $\frac{2}{3}(6h - 1)$

9. $(-3.2x + 2.1)(-6)$

10. $3.5(3x - 8)$

11. $4(x + 7)$

12. $-2.5(2a - 4)$

13. $\frac{2}{3}(12 - 15d)$

14. $-2(k - 11)$

15. $-\frac{1}{3}(6h + 15)$

16. $(2c - 8)(-4)$

17. $-(4 - 2b)$

18. $2(3x - 9)$

19. $4(2r + 8)$

20. $-5(b - 5)$

21. $3(f + 2)$

22. $6h + 5(h - 5)$

23. $-5d + 3(2d - 7)$

24. $7 + 2(4x - 3)$

25. $2(3h + 2) - 4h$

26. $2(4 + y)$

27. $\frac{1}{2}(2n - 4) - 2n$

28. $-w + 4(w + 3)$

29. $0.4(3d - 5)$

30. $-4d + 2(3 + d)$

31. $2x + \frac{3}{4}(4x + 16)$

32. $2(3a + 2)$

33. $5(t - 3) - 2t$

34. $5(b + 4) - 6b$

35. $\frac{2}{5}(5k + 35) - 8$

36. $0.4(2s + 4)$

37. $\frac{2}{3}(9b - 27)$

38. $\frac{1}{2}(12n - 8)$

39. $0.5(2x - 4)$

40. $2(a - 4) + 15$

41. $13 + 2(5c - 2)$

42. $7 + 2(\frac{1}{5}a - 3)$

43. $5(3x + 12)$

44. $2(m + 1)$

45. $4(2a + 2) - 17$

46. $-4x + 3(2x - 5)$

47. $3(t - 12)$

48. $-6 - 3(2k + 4)$

Write an expression for each phrase.

49. 5 times the quantity x plus 6

50. twice the quantity y minus 8

51. the product of -15 and the quantity x minus 5

52. 32 divided by the quantity y plus 12

53. -8 times the quantity 4 decreased by w

54. the quantity x plus 9 times the quantity 7 minus x

Practice 1-9

Name the coordinates of each point on the graph at the right.

1. A

2. B

3. C

4. D

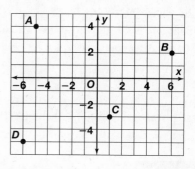

In which quadrant would you find each point?

5. $(-3, 4)$

6. $(-6, -6)$

7. $(1, 5)$

8. $(8, -9)$

Use the data in each table to draw a scatter plot.

9. **Height and Hourly Pay of Ten People**

Height (inches)	Hourly Pay	Height (inches)	Hourly Pay
62	$6.00	72	$8.00
65	$8.50	72	$6.00
68	$6.50	73	$7.50
70	$6.00	74	$6.25
70	$7.50	74	$8.00

10. **Speed of Winds in Some U.S. Cities**

Station	Average Speed (mi/h)	Highest Speed (mi/h)
Atlanta, GA	9.1	60
Casper, WY	12.9	81
Dallas, TX	10.7	73
Mobile, AL	9.0	63
St. Louis, MO	9.7	60

Source: National Climatic Data Center

11. In Exercise 9, is there a *positive correlation*, a *negative correlation*, or *no correlation* between height and hourly pay?

12. In Exercise 10, is there a *positive correlation*, a *negative correlation*, or *no correlation* between average wind speed and highest wind speed?

Would you expect a *positive correlation*, a *negative correlation*, or *no correlation* between the two data sets? Why?

13. a person's age and the number of pets he or she has

14. the number of times you brush your teeth and the number of cavities you get

15. the number of days it rains per year and the number of umbrellas sold

Is there a *positive correlation*, a *negative correlation*, or *no correlation* between the two data sets in each scatter plot?

16.

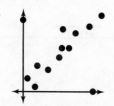

17.

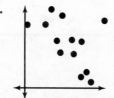

18.

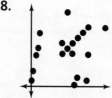

Reteaching 1-1

OBJECTIVE: Using variables as a shorthand way of expressing relationships

MATERIALS: None

You often hear word phrases such as *half as much* or *three times as deep*. These phrases describe mathematical relationships. You can translate word phrases like these into mathematical relationships called *expressions*.

Example

Translate the following word expressions into algebraic expressions.

the sum of x and 15
$x + 15$
Remember that "sum" means to add.

seven times x
$7x$
Remember that "times" mean to multiply.

Example

Translate the following word sentence into an algebraic equation.

The weight of the truck is two times the weight of the car.

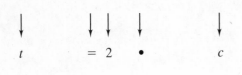

The weight of the truck is two times the weight of the car.

| | | | | |
| t | $=$ | 2 | $\bullet$ | c |

$t = 2c$

← Write an equal sign under the word *is*. Whatever is written to the left of *is* belongs on the left side of the =. Whatever is written to the right of *is* belongs on the right side of the =.

← **Represent the unknown amounts with variables.**

← **The translation is complete. Check to make sure you have translated all parts of the equation.**

Exercises

Translate the following word expressions and sentences into algebraic expressions or equations.

1. a number increased by 5

2. 8 subtracted from a number

3. a number divided by 9

4. 3 less than five times a number

5. A number multiplied by 12 is 84.

6. 7 less than n is 22.

7. 8 times a number x is 72.

8. A number divided by 3 is 18.

Reteaching 1-2

Exponents and Order of Operations

•••

OBJECTIVE: Using the order of operations	**MATERIALS:** Three index cards or small pieces of paper

Review the order of operations to help you with this activity.

Order of Operations
1. Perform any operations inside grouping symbols.
2. Simplify any term with exponents.
3. Multiply and divide in order from left to right.
4. Add and subtract in order from left to right.

Example

Write $+$ on the first index card, $-$ on the second card, and $\times$ on the third card. Shuffle the cards and place them face down on your desk. Randomly pick cards to fill in the blanks with operation signs. Once you have filled in the operation signs, simplify the expression.

$6\_\_\_(9\_\_\_7)\_\_\_8$ $\longleftarrow$ **Pick cards to fill in the blanks with operation signs.**

$6 \times (9 - 7) + 8$ $\longleftarrow$ **Subtract 7 from 9 inside the grouping symbols.**

$6 \times \quad 2 \quad + 8$ $\longleftarrow$ **Do multiplication and division first. Multiply 6 by 2.**

$12 \qquad + 8$ $\longleftarrow$ **Do addition and subtraction last. Add 12 and 8 to get the answer.**

20 $\longleftarrow$ **The answer is 20.**

Exercises

Randomly pick cards to fill in the operation symbols of the following expressions. Simplify the expressions.

1. $7\_\_\_\_5\_\_\_\_1$

2. $(3\_\_\_\_9)\_\_\_\_4$

3. $8\_\_\_\_2\_\_\_\_(5\_\_\_\_10)$

4. $(3\_\_\_\_7\_\_\_\_6)\_\_\_\_1$

Simplify each expression by following the order of operations.

5. $(5 \cdot 3) - 18$

6. $5 \cdot (3 - 18)$

7. $2 \cdot (27 - 13 \cdot 2)$

8. $2 \cdot 27 - 13 \cdot 2$

9. $18 \div (9 - 15 \div 5)$

10. $18 \div 9 - 15 \div 5$

11. $2 \cdot 8 - 6^2$

12. $2 \cdot (8 - 6^2)$

Reteaching 1-3

Exploring Real Numbers

• •

OBJECTIVE: Classifying numbers	**MATERIALS:** None

Review the following chart which shows the different classifications of real numbers.

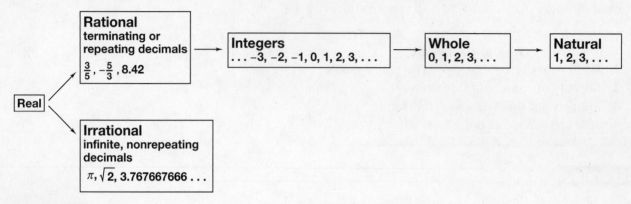

Example

Given the numbers $-4.4, \frac{14}{5}, 0, -9, 1\frac{1}{4}, -\pi$ and 32, tell which numbers belong to each set.

Natural:	32	numbers used to count
Whole:	0, 32	natural numbers and zero
Integers:	0, −9, 32	whole numbers and their opposites
Rational:	$-4.4, \frac{14}{5}, 0, -9, 1\frac{1}{4}, 32$	integers and terminating and nonrepeating decimals
Irrational:	$-\pi$	infinite, nonrepeating decimals
Real:	$-4.4, \frac{14}{5}, 0, -9, 1\frac{1}{4}, -\pi, 32$	rational and irrational numbers

Exercises

Name the set(s) of numbers to which each number belongs.

1. $\frac{-5}{6}$ **2.** 35.99   **3.** 0   **4.** $4\frac{1}{8}$

5. $\sqrt{5}$ **6.** −80   **7.** $\frac{17}{5}$ **8.** $\frac{12}{3}$

9. $\sqrt{100}$ **10.** $-\sqrt{4}$ **11.** 3.24   **12.** 3π

Give an example of each kind of number.

13. irrational number

14. whole number

15. negative integer

16. fractional rational number

17. rational decimal

18. natural number

Reteaching 1-4

OBJECTIVE: Adding integers and decimals	**MATERIALS:** None

Review the following addition rules.

- To add two numbers with the same sign, *add* their absolute values. The sum has the same sign as the numbers.

- To add two numbers with different signs, find the *difference* of their absolute values. The sum has the same sign as the number with the greater absolute value.

Example

The following example shows you step by step how to add two numbers with different signs.

$-6 + 2$

$6 - 2$ ← **Find the difference of their absolute values.**

4 ← **Subtract.**

-4 ← **Since −6 has the greater absolute value, the answer takes the negative sign.**

Exercises

Simplify. Be sure to check the sign of your answer.

1. $-3 + (-4)$ **2.** $12 + 5$ **3.** $-5 + 8$ **4.** $-8 + (-2)$

5. $-2 + (-3)$ **6.** $9 + (-12)$ **7.** $-3 + 5$ **8.** $-4 + 3$

9. $-2.3 + (-1.5)$ **10.** $4.5 + 3.1$ **11.** $-5.1 + 2.8$ **12.** $13.9 + 7.3$

13. $1.3 + (-1.1)$ **14.** $-3.6 + (-6.7)$ **15.** $1.4 + (-21.4)$ **16.** $-9.8 + 3.5$

Evaluate each expression for $a = 5$ and $b = -4$.

17. $-a + (-b)$ **18.** $-a + b$ **19.** $a + b$ **20.** $a + (-b)$

Evaluate each expression for $h = 3.4$.

21. $2.5 + h$ **22.** $-2.5 + h$ **23.** $2.5 + (-h)$ **24.** $-2.5 + (-h)$

25. $h + 7.1$ **26.** $-h + 7.1$ **27.** $h + (-7.1)$ **28.** $-h + (-7.1)$

Reteaching 1-5

Subtracting Real Numbers

OBJECTIVE: Subtracting integers and decimals   **MATERIALS:** None

Review the following subtraction rules.

- To subtract a number, rewrite the problem to add the opposite of the number.

- Follow the rules for addition of numbers.

Example

The following example shows you step by step how to subtract two numbers.

$$5 - 11$$

$5 + (-11)$ ⟵ **Rewrite the problem to add the opposite of the number.**

$11 - 5$ ⟵ **Find the difference of their absolute values.**

6 ⟵ **Subtract.**

-6 ⟵ **Since -11 has the greater absolute value, the answer takes the negative sign.**

Exercises

Simplify. Be sure to check the sign of your answer.

1. $7 - 12$ **2.** $6 - 9$ **3.** $4 - (-5)$ **4.** $7 - (-3)$

5. $-6 - 4$ **6.** $-7 - 2$ **7.** $-5 - (-4)$ **8.** $-3 - (-10)$

9. $-3.1 - (-5.4)$ **10.** $8.3 - 5.1$ **11.** $-7.8 - 6.6$ **12.** $-4.8 - 2.5$

13. $8.7 - 2.5$ **14.** $-4.6 - (-3)$ **15.** $-9.3 - (-8.1)$ **16.** $-9.9 - 3.8$

Evaluate each expression for $a = -4$ and $b = 3$.

17. $a - b$ **18.** $-a - b$ **19.** $a - (-b)$ **20.** $-a - (-b)$

21. $3b - a$ **22.** $-|b|$ **23.** $|a - b|$ **24.** $|a| - 3|b|$

Subtract. (Hint: Subtract corresponding elements.)

25. $\begin{bmatrix} -3 & -2 \\ 0 & 1 \end{bmatrix} - \begin{bmatrix} 3 & 1 \\ 2 & 4 \end{bmatrix}$

26. $\begin{bmatrix} \frac{1}{2} \\ -1 \end{bmatrix} - \begin{bmatrix} \frac{2}{3} \\ -3 \end{bmatrix}$

Reteaching 1-6

Multiplying and Dividing Real Numbers

OBJECTIVE: Multiplying and dividing integers and decimals

MATERIALS: A number cube

Review the following multiplication and division rules.

- The product or quotient of two positive numbers is always positive.
- The product or quotient of two negative numbers is always positive.
- The product or quotient of a positive and a negative number is always negative.

Example

Roll the number cube to determine the signs of the numbers in the following example. If you roll an even number (2, 4, or 6), write $+$ in the blank to make the number positive. If you roll an odd number (1, 3, or 5), write a $-$ in the blank to make the number negative. Decide what sign the answer will have before you calculate the answer.

____ 56 ÷ ____ 7 ← **Roll the number cube to fill in the blanks.**

$-56 \div (+7)$ ← **Suppose your first roll was a 3, so 56 is negative. Suppose your second roll was 6, so 7 is positive. Now that you have the signs of the numbers, decide what the sign of the answer will be. Dividing a negative number by a positive number results in a negative number.**

-8 ← **The answer is -8.**

Exercises

Roll the number cube to determine the signs of the numbers in the following exercises. Remember to decide what sign the answer will have before you calculate the answer.

1. ____ 20 · ____ 8

2. ____ 3.2 · ____ 10

3. ____ 27 ÷ ____ 3

4. ____ 14 · ____ 4

5. ____ 120 ÷ ____ 12

6. ____ 45 ÷ ____ 9

7. ____ 1.4 · ____ 3

8. ____ 96 ÷ ____ 8

Simplify each expression.

9. $4(-2)$

10. $-6(12)$

11. $-2(-5)$

12. $-8(11)$

13. $(-7)^2$

14. $-10(-5)$

Reteaching 1-7

The Distributive Property

OBJECTIVE: Using the Distributive Property	**MATERIALS:** None

You can compare the Distributive Property to distributing paper to the class. Just as you distribute a piece of paper to each person in the class, you distribute the number immediately outside the parentheses to each term inside the parentheses by multiplying.

Example

Simplify $3(2x + 3)$ by using the Distributive Property.

$3(2x + 3)$ ⟵   **Draw arrows to show that 3 is distributed to the 2x and to the 3.**

$3(2x) + 3(3)$ ⟵   **Use the Distributive Property.**

$6x + 9$ ⟵   **Simplify.**

Example

Simplify $-(4x + 7)$ by using the Distributive Property.

$-1(4x + 7)$ ⟵   **Rewrite using the Multiplication Property of −1.**

$-1(4x + 7)$ ⟵   **Draw arrows to show that −1 is distributed to the 4x and to the 7.**

$-1(4x) + (-1)(7)$ ⟵   **Use the Distributive Property.**

$-4x - 7$ ⟵   **Simplify.**

Exercises

Draw arrows to show the Distributive Property. Then simplify each expression.

1. $2(5x + 4)$ **2.** $\frac{1}{4}(12x - 8)$ **3.** $4(7x - 3)$

4. $5(4 + 2x)$ **5.** $6(5 - 3x)$ **6.** $0.1(30x - 50)$

7. $(2x - 4)3$ **8.** $(3x + 4)7$ **9.** $8(x + y)$

10. $-(4x + 3)$ **11.** $-(-2x + 1)$ **12.** $-(-6x - 3)$

13. $-(14x - 3)$ **14.** $-(-7x - 1)$ **15.** $-(3x + 4)$

Reteaching 1-8

OBJECTIVE: Recognizing properties	**MATERIALS:** None

The properties of real numbers allow you to write equivalent expressions.

The Commutative Properties of Addition and Multiplication allow you to add or to multiply two numbers in any order.

$$a + b = b + a \qquad\qquad a \cdot b = b \cdot a$$

$$3 + 6 = 6 + 3 \qquad\qquad 12 \cdot 4 = 4 \cdot 12$$

The Associative Properties of Addition and Multiplication allow you to regroup numbers.

$$(a + b) + c = a + (b + c) \qquad (a \cdot b) \cdot c = a \cdot (b \cdot c)$$

$$(1 + 3) + 6 = 1 + (3 + 6) \qquad (1 \cdot 3) \cdot 6 = 1 \cdot (3 \cdot 6)$$

The Distributive Property distributes multiplication over addition and subtraction.

$$a(b + c) = ab + ac \qquad\qquad a(b - c) = ab - ac$$

$$3(4 + 6) = (3 \cdot 4) + (3 \cdot 6) \qquad 5(9 - 3) = (5 \cdot 9) - (5 \cdot 3)$$

Example

Name the property that each equation illustrates.

$72 + 56 = 56 + 72$ ← **Commutative Property of Addition: The order of the addends is changed.**

$4(5 - 9) = (4 \cdot 5) - (4 \cdot 9)$ ← **Distributive Property: The 4 is distributed.**

$30 \cdot (14 \cdot 5) = (30 \cdot 14) \cdot 5$ ← **Associative Property of Multiplication: The numbers are regrouped.**

Exercises

Name the property that each equation illustrates.

1. $(17 + 4) + 9 = 17 + (4 + 9)$ **2.** $7(3 + 4) = (7 \cdot 3) + (7 \cdot 4)$

3. $84 \cdot 26 = 26 \cdot 84$ **4.** $(3 \cdot 6) \cdot 7 = 3 \cdot (6 \cdot 7)$

5. $8(6 - 3) = (8 \cdot 6) - (8 \cdot 3)$ **6.** $4.2 + 3.4 = 3.4 + 4.2$

Write the number that makes each statement true.

7. $27 + \underline{\quad} = 12 + 27$ **8.** $(8 + 20) + 9 = \underline{\quad} + (20 + 9)$

9. $9(8 - 5) = (\underline{\quad} \cdot 8) - (\underline{\quad} \cdot 5)$ **10.** $8 \cdot 10 = 10 \cdot \underline{\quad}$

11. $3 \cdot (9 \cdot 6) = (3 \cdot 9) \cdot \underline{\quad}$ **12.** $7(6 + 4) = (\underline{\quad} \cdot 6) + (\underline{\quad} \cdot 4)$

Name _____ Class _____ Date _____

Reteaching 1-9

Graphing Data on the Coordinate Plane

OBJECTIVE: Identifying coordinates on the coordinate plane

MATERIALS: Graph paper

Coordinates give the location of a point. To locate a point (x, y) on a graph, start at the origin, $(0, 0)$. Move x units to the right or to the left along the x-axis and y units up or down along the y-axis.

Example

Give the coordinates of points A, B, C, and D.

Point A is 2 units to the left of the origin and 3 units up. The coordinates of A are $(-2, 3)$.

Point B is 2 units to the right of the origin and 2 units up. The coordinates of B are $(2, 2)$.

Point C is 4 units to the left of the origin and 0 units up. The coordinates of C are $(-4, 0)$.

Point D is 1 unit to the left of the origin and 3 units down. The coordinates of D are $(-1, -3)$.

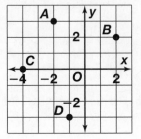

Exercises

Name the coordinates of each point.

1. G

2. H

3. J

4. K

5. L

6. M

7. N

8. P

9. Q

10. R

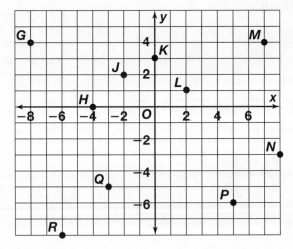

Graph the points on the same coordinate plane.

11. $S\ (3, -5)$

12. $T\ (0, 0)$

13. $U\ (-1, -2)$

14. $V\ (4, 5)$

15. $W\ (0, 3)$

16. $Z\ (-5, 0)$

Enrichment 1-1

Expressing Relationship Using Variables

Variables can be used to express the relationship between input and output of most computing machines. For example, the relationship between the input and output found on this printout sheet is output = input + 7. If I represents the input and O the output, then the relationship is $O = I + 7$.

INPUT	OUTPUT
4	11
5	12
6	13
7	14

Sometimes the input and output have special variable names that are used to identify the quantities that make up the relationships.

For the printout sheets below, determine the relationships and express them using variables.

1.

INPUT	OUTPUT
3	7
4	9
5	11
6	13
7	15

2.

INPUT	OUTPUT
9	26
11	32
13	38
15	44
17	50

3.

INPUT	OUTPUT
1	0
2	3
3	8
4	15
5	24

4.

T	S
0	0
1	16
2	64
3	144
4	256

5.

T	R
12	16
16	19
20	22
24	25
26	26.5

6.

E	P
1	3
2	5
3	9
4	17
5	33

7. Prepare a printout sheet with a particular relationship. Then have one of your classmates determine what the relationship is.

Enrichment 1-2
· ·
Mystery Signs

Look at the equation 5 # 3 = 8. Although the meaning of the symbol "#" is not known, your knowledge of arithmetic tells you that # must mean addition because 5 + 3 = 8.

Now look at the equation 2 △ 2 = 4. If you think that △ means addition, you could be right because 2 + 2 = 4. However, △ could also mean multiplication because 2 × 2 = 4. And, △ could also mean "raise to the power of" because $2^2 = 4$.

In each of the follow exercises, the symbols #, △, @, and * can represent any of the operations listed in the chart at the right. Once you have determined the meaning of each "mystery sign," rewrite the equation using familiar operation symbols. The mystery signs may represent different operations in different exercises. However, if a symbol is repeated in an exercise, it represents the same operation each time it appears in that exercise. More than one solution is possible for at least one exercise.

| ADD |
| SUBTRACT |
| MULTIPLY |
| DIVIDE |
| RAISE TO THE POWER OF . . . |
| TAKE THE SQUARE ROOT OF . . . |

1. 3 # 2 # 2 = 12 _____

2. △(8 * 8) = 4 _____

3. 2 △ 3 = 8 _____

4. (3 @ 7) # 4 = 40 _____

5. (3 # 6) * 3 = 3 _____

6. 30 * 6 # 5 = 25 _____

7. (3 * 9) # 2 = 25 _____

8. 4 # 3 @ 2 = 13 _____

9. (10 # 2) + (3 * 3) = 14 _____

10. @ 25 * 3 # 2 # 1 = 12 _____

11. (5 # 3 @ 4) * 3 = 12 _____

12. 3 @ (8 * 2) = 18 _____

13. (4 * 4) # (2 * 4) △ 6 = 18 _____

Enrichment 1-3
Newspaper Scavenger Hunt

Examples of numbers can be found in many newspapers and magazines that are read every day.

Look through newspapers and magazines to find the following items. When you locate an item, cut it out and fasten it to poster board or a notebook. Be sure to label each item.

- an integer greater than 100
- an integer less than 100
- a number written in words
- a percent
- a positive rational number
- a negative rational number
- an irrational number
- a decimal (not money)
- a numeral less than 1
- a negative integer
- a negative non-integer
- a whole number
- a percent larger than 100%
- an example of multiplication of real numbers
- an example of division of real numbers
- an example of addition of real numbers
- an example of subtraction of real numbers
- an example of a coordinate plane or scatter plot

In many instances, the same item can be used more than once.

List below any other examples of interesting numbers or calculations that you found.

Name _____ Class _____ Date _____

Enrichment 1-4
....
The Checker Model of Addition of Integers

Integers can be represented by checkers. Let black checkers represent positive integers.

3 can be represented by

9 can be represented by

Red checkers can represent negative integers.

−5 can be represented by

○ ○ ○ ○ ○

−2 can be represented by

○ ○

Notice, however, that the representation is not unique. If you think of the black and red checkers as protons and electrons of equal charge that can neutralize each other, then other representations are possible.

3 can be represented by

−5 can be represented by

Zero can be represented in many ways. Here are two of them:

(no checkers)   ● ●
                 ○ ○

Addition can also be represented using checkers.

$$5 \quad + \quad (-8) \quad = \quad -3$$

 ○○○○ ○○○
          ○○○○

1. The representation above is not unique. Show another way to add 5 + (−8).

Represent each integer at least two ways using checkers.

2. 4   **3.** 6

4. −4   **5.** −1

Show the sums using checkers.

6. 7 + 5   **7.** −13 + 8

8. −6 + (−9)   **9.** 0 + 11

10. 3 + 8   **11.** −7 + (−3) + 12

Algebra 1 Chapter 1

Enrichment 1-5

Integer Football

MATERIALS: 2 number cubes of different colors, place marker or chip

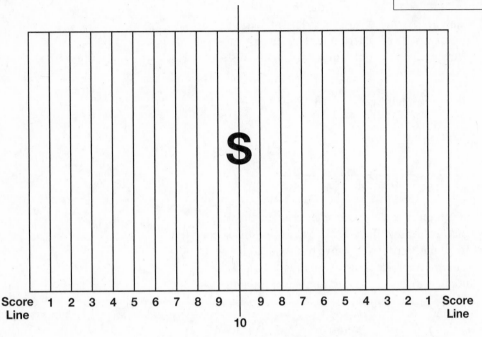

On the game board, the S represents the starting position at the beginning of the game and the position to which a player returns after scoring. The object of the game is to move your marker to or across your own score line for a touchdown.

Before beginning, decide the following:

- Which number cube represents positive integers and which number cube represents negative integers?
- Which player will go first?
- What score must be reached to win?

To Play

The player rolls both number cubes. The player finds the sum of the numbers on the cubes, remembering that one number is positive and one number is negative. The player moves his/her marker toward or away from his/her score line depending on whether the sum is positive or negative. Repeat this procedure four more times. A player's turn consists of five rolls or a touchdown.

To Score

On a sheet of paper divided into two columns, keep track of each player's rolls as well as the number of touchdowns earned.

- A player who lands on or past his/her score line within the five rolls, is awarded a touchdown.
- If a player lands on or past his/her opponent's score line within the five rolls, the opponent is awarded a touchdown.
- If a player lands somewhere on the field after five rolls, his/her opponent takes possession and begins his/her turn.
- The player who first reaches or goes over the agreed-upon score is the winner.

Enrichment 1-6
Factorials

A citywide club is having a dinner for all its members. The members of the Board of Directors are supposed to sit at one side of the front table. This table is rectangular in shape and has room for all 8 board members. Someone forgot to put the name tags at the places, so the directors can choose any chair they wish. How many different seating arrangements are possible?

If each position at the table is represented by a number, you can represent the table like this:

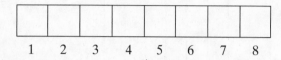

Since no one has been seated yet, there are 8 possible choices for the first seat. Once the first person has been seated, there are 7 ways to fill the second seat. There are then 6 ways to fill the third seat, 5 ways to fill the fourth seat, and so on. To find the total possible number of arrangements, all these possible choices must be multiplied together. So the number of possible arrangements is $8 \times 7 \times 6 \times 5 \times 4 \times 3 \times 2 \times 1$.

This multiplication can be represented by the expression 8!, which is read "eight factorial."

$1! = 1$

$4! = 4 \times 3 \times 2 \times 1 = 24$

In general, for any positive integer n,
$n! = n \times (n - 1) \times (n - 2) \times \ldots \times 2 \times 1$

Compute.

1. $6!$

2. $(12 - 7)!$

3. $3! \times 4! \times 5!$

4. $\dfrac{6!}{5!}$

5. $\dfrac{5!}{(7 - 4)!}$

6. $\dfrac{(6 - 2)!}{2! \times 2!}$

7. Suppose that a state uses only the even digits, 0, 2, 4, 6, 8, to create license numbers for motorbikes. How many different four-digit license plates could be made if no digit can be repeated?

8. How many different five-digit license plates could be made if the digits cannot be repeated?

9. How many four-digit license plates could be made if the digits can be repeated?

Enrichment 1-7

The Distributive Property and a Number Puzzle

Examine the following number puzzle and example.

Pick a number.	4
Add 2 to the number.	6
Multiply the result by 3.	18
Subtract 3 from the result.	15
Divide the result by 3.	5
Subtract 1 from the result.	4

Notice that the final result is the same number as the starting number.

1. Try the puzzle starting with the number 10. Do you end up with 10 as the final result?

2. Try the puzzle starting with −3. Do you end up with −3 as the final result?

For the following puzzles, choose 3 or 4 numbers to start with and note the results. What conclusion can you make about the results for each puzzle?

3. Pick a number.
   Add 5 to the number.
   Multiply the result by 4.
   Subtract 12 from the result.
   Divide the result by 4.
   Subtract your original number.
   What is the result?

4. Pick a number.
   Multiply the number by 10.
   Add 5 to the result.
   Double the result.
   Subtract 10 from the result.
   Divide the result by 2.
   What is the result?

An explanation of why the puzzles work the way they do can be determined by using a variable rather than a specific number.

For example, the puzzle at the top of the page can be solved algebraically using x as the starting number.

Pick a number.	x	
Add 2 to the number.	$x + 2$	
Multiply the result by 3.	$3(x + 2) = 3x + 6$	⟶ Note the use
Subtract 3 from the result.	$3(x + 2) - 3 = 3x + 3$	of the Distributive
Divide the result by 3.	$x + 1$	Property.
Subtract 1 from the result.	x	

The final result will be the same as the starting number.

5. Determine the algebraic solution for the puzzles in Exercises 3–4.

Name_____ Class_____ Date_____

Enrichment 1-8
Clock Multiplication and Division

Consider a seven-hour clock. Instead of using the numbers 1 to 12, it uses the numbers 0 to 6. Multiplication in this system is defined as repeated addition. So, 3×4 means $4 + 4 + 4$. On the clock, begin at 0 and move 4 hours in the clockwise direction 3 times. It is then 5 o'clock. This means that $3 \times 4 = 5$ in the seven-hour clock system.

In this system, $2 \times 5 = 5 + 5 = 3$.

The multiplicative identity in this system is 1, so the multiplicative inverse of 2 is 4 because $2 \times 4 = 1$.

Because $5 \times 2 = 3, 3 \div 2 = 5$.

Compute the following using the seven-hour clock system.

1. 3×6

2. 5×5

3. $3 \times 6 \times 4$

4. $5 \times (4 + 3)$

5. $(2 + 6) \times 5$

6. $(4 + 2) \times (3 + 1)$

7. $6 \div 1$

8. $3 \div 3$

9. Demonstrate that 1 is the multiplicative identity of the seven-hour clock system.

10. Find the multiplicative inverse of each digit in the seven-hour clock system.

Compute the following using a six-hour clock system.

11. 3×1

12. $5 \times (4 \times 2)$

13. $2 \times 3 \times (0 \times 4)$

14. $3 \times (4 + 4)$

15. 0×2

16. $(4 \times 2) + 3$

17. $(3 \times 2) + 4$

18. $(4 + 1) \times 4$

19. $(2 \times 5) + (0 \times 1)$

20. $(4 \div 4) + (3 \times 2)$

© Pearson Education, Inc. All rights reserved.

26 Lesson 1-8 Enrichment *Algebra 1* Chapter 1

Enrichment 1-9

Polar Coordinates

Another type of coordinate system used in plotting points and graphing equations is called a **polar coordinate system.** The system is composed of equally spaced concentric circles, centered at a point called the **pole.**

Points in this system are described as ordered pairs, (r, θ), where $|r|$ indicates the distance from the pole and θ is an angle measured from the **polar axis.** A positive value of θ indicates an angle measured in a counter-clockwise direction from the polar axis. A negative value of θ indicates an angle measured in a clockwise direction from the polar axis.

To graph ordered pairs with negative r values, graph $(|r|, \theta + 180°)$. The graph below at the right shows the location of the points $(3, 45°), (5, 120°)$ and $(-2, 90°)$.

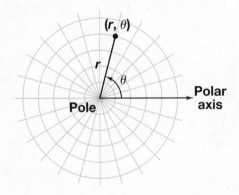
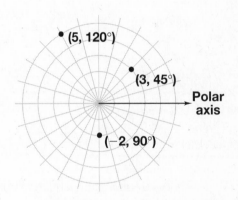

Determine the location of the following ordered pairs and plot the points on the polar coordinate system.

1. $(4, 30°)$ **2.** $(3, 210°)$ **6.** $(-1, 60°)$ **7.** $(-2, 180°)$

3. $(2, 180°)$ **4.** $(1, 0°)$ **8.** $(-5, 75°)$ **9.** $(1.5, 270°)$

5. $(5, -180°)$ **10.** $(4, -235°)$

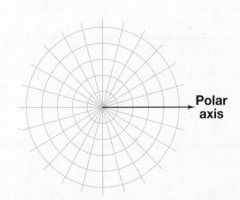

Chapter 1 Project: Taking Stock

Beginning the Chapter Project

How do stockbrokers and financial analysts determine what stocks to buy? What do they investigate when looking at a company?

As you work through the activities, you will collect data about a company. You will use formulas to analyze the data. Then you will decide how to organize and display your results in graphs and spreadsheets. The activities will help you better understand how stockbrokers and financial analysts track stock performance to determine what stocks to buy.

List of Materials

- Calculator
- Newspaper
- Graph paper

Activities

Activity 1: Researching
Before making any decisions regarding a stock purchase, it is customary to obtain facts and a history about a company.

- Select a company to research. Gather information about the products or services the company sells, the history of the company, its management practices, and its revenue and profits.

- What is the stock symbol and on which market is it traded?

- Investigate the requirements for a company to trade on the New York Stock Exchange.

Activity 2: Analyzing
Before you can track a stock, you need to be familiar with the stock page of the newspaper.

- Using a newspaper with a stock page, determine what the headings mean for each column.

- Find the closing price for the stock you chose in Activity 1.

- What was the highest price for that stock during the last year?

Chapter 1 Project (continued)

Activity 3: Organizing

Ideally, before buying stock in a company, you study the historical performance of the stock in order to help predict its future potential. In this activity you will track a stock's performance during previous years.

- Using the company you selected in Activity 1, create a spreadsheet that displays the high and low price for the year, and earnings per share. The information should be collected for the last 10 years (if the stock has been traded for 10 years).

- Include a row on the spreadsheet that determines the average of each column.

Activity 4: Calculating

Suppose you have $5000 to invest in the stock you have selected. The purchase price will include the price of the stock plus a $19.95 fee.

- How many shares of stock can you buy?
- Keep track of your stock daily. Did the stock close higher or lower than the day before?
- Prepare a graph of the daily closing prices of your stock for the duration of the project.
- At the conclusion of the project, suppose you sell your stock. Did you make a profit or incur a loss? Explain.

Finishing the Project

The answers to the four activities should help you complete your project. Assemble all the parts of your project in a folder. Include a summary of what you have learned about the stock market. Is the stock you picked a good stock? Would you recommend this stock to others? Explain.

Reflect and Revise

Ask a classmate to review your notebook with you. Together, check that your graph is clearly labeled and accurate. Check that your calculations are accurate. Is your spreadsheet well organized and easy to follow? Make any necessary revisions to improve your work.

Extending the Project

Investigate the advantages of diversifying your stock portfolio. What do stockbrokers and financial analysts recommend in regards to purchasing a particular stock?

 **Take it to the NET**

Visit PHSchool.com for information and links you might find helpful as you complete your project.

Chapter Project Manager

....

Chapter 1: Taking Stock

Getting Started

Read the project. As you work on the project, you will need a calculator, a
newspaper, and materials to make an accurate and attractive graph. Keep all
of your work for the project in a folder.

Checklist

☐ Activity 1: researching a company

☐ Activity 2: tracking the stock

☐ Activity 3: creating a spreadsheet

☐ Activity 4: determining profit or loss

☐ project display

Suggestions

☐ Look up the information at the library or on
the Internet.

☐ Ask an adult for additional help interpreting the
stock page.

☐ Gather all the necessary information. Consider
checking financial advisers' web sites.

☐ Recall that profit is the money remaining after
expenses have been paid.

☐ Was the financial history of the company you
researched a good indicator of your stock's overall
performance? How might your spreadsheet and
graph be useful in predicting future performance
of your stock?

Scoring Rubric

3 Answers to all questions, explanations, and calculations are clear and
easy to follow. The spreadsheet is well organized, clear, and includes all
information. The graph is clear and includes all information with
appropriate scales and labeled axes.

2 Answers to all questions, explanations, and calculations are essentially
correct, but may contain some incorrect information. The spreadsheet
and graph are clear, but may contain some minor errors in organization,
computation, or scale.

1 Answers, explanations, and calculations are difficult to follow or
misleading. The spreadsheet and graph are difficult to follow or missing
important information.

0 Major elements of the project are incomplete or missing.

Your Evaluation of Project Evaluate your work, based on the *Scoring Rubric*.

Teacher's Evaluation of Project

Chapter Project Teacher Notes
Chapter 1: Taking Stock

About the Project
The project gives students an opportunity to explore the connection between math and the stock market. The activities will help students understand how to investigate a stock and evaluate the history of a stock.

Introducing the Project
- Ask students to work with partners or in small groups. Discuss the fact that most people rely on information from organizations to determine whether investing in a company's stock is a good risk.
- Discuss where the students can look to complete their research. Suggestions might include libraries, on-line services, stockbrokers, and annual reports.
- Encourage students to make a list of companies they want to investigate.

Activity 1: Researching
Students will gather information about companies whose stocks they are interested in purchasing.

Activity 2: Analyzing
Students will determine what each column on the stock page of a newspaper means.

Activity 3: Organizing
Students will create spreadsheets to record the historical performances of the stocks they are considering.

Activity 4: Calculating
Students will buy $5000 worth of stock in the company they selected. They will track and graph the stocks' daily closing price.

Finishing the Project
You may wish to plan a project day on which students share their completed projects. Encourage groups to explain their processes as well as their results. Have students review their project work and update their folders.

- Have students review their methods for finding, recording, and displaying the data they needed for their projects.
- Ask groups to share their insights that resulted from completing the project, such as any shortcuts they found for making graphs and spreadsheets. Also, ask if any mathematical ideas have become more obvious and if there are areas about which the students would like to learn more.

 **Take it to the NET**

Visit PHSchool.com for information, student links, and teacher support for this project.

✔ Checkpoint Quiz 1

Use with Lessons 1-1 through 1-4.

Write a variable expression for each phrase. Then evaluate the expression
for $x = 4$, $y = -3$, and $z = 1.4$.

1. 14 increased by x

2. the product of z and 5

3. the sum of x and y

4. the quotient of 24 and x

5. 4 times z

6. 10 more than the sum of y and z

7. y plus twice x

8. the product of x and z

Is each statement *true* or *false*? If the statement is false, give a
counterexample.

9. The *opposite* of the *opposite* of a negative number is a positive number.

10. The set of whole numbers is reasonable to use to record the daily
temperature of Boston, Massachusetts.

- - - - ✂ -

✔ Checkpoint Quiz 2

Use with Lessons 1-5 through 1-8.

Simplify each expression.

1. $8 + 4w + 3 + w$

2. $(6 \cdot 12) \cdot 3$

3. $(3 + 22)4$

4. $(-3)^2 + (-4)(-9)$

5. $-3(7 + w) - 5w$

6. $-(-6 - 5x)$

7. $|4.3 + (-7.2)|$

8. $12 \div (-4) - 5 \div (-10)$

9. $5x + 4y - 11x - 2y$

10. a. Simplify the expression $4w + 7(w + 3)$.
Justify each step.
b. Evaluate the expression for $w = -4$.

Chapter Test

Form A

Chapter 1

Write an equation to model the relationship in each table.

1.

Number of Months	Amount Saved
1	$150
2	$300
3	$450
4	$600

2.

Distance Traveled	Distance Remaining
10 mi	90 mi
25 mi	75 mi
40 mi	60 mi
88 mi	12 mi

Simplify.

3. $4 + 8 \div 2 + 6 \times 2$

4. $12 - (-3)$

5. $-6(-3) + -2$

6. $(-8)^2 \div (-2)$

Evaluate each expression.

7. $5x + 4$ for $x = 5$

8. $y^2 \div z$ for $y = -12$ and $z = -9$

9. $|6 - 2m|$ for $m = 7$

10. $-2(2s - 3t)$ for $s = -5.2$ and $t = 1.9$

11. $\frac{a}{b}$ for $a = \frac{2}{3}$ and $b = -\frac{5}{6}$

12. $\frac{2d - 3}{-5}$ for $d = 9$

Find the sum or difference.

13. $\begin{bmatrix} -2 & 13 \\ 8 & -6 \end{bmatrix} + \begin{bmatrix} 8 & -17 \\ -8 & -4 \end{bmatrix}$

14. $\begin{bmatrix} 1.2 & -6.8 \\ 0.4 & 0 \\ 2.3 & -8 \end{bmatrix} - \begin{bmatrix} 2.5 & 3.6 \\ -2.7 & -0.1 \\ 2.4 & -7.3 \end{bmatrix}$

Is each statement *true* or *false*? If the statement is false, give a counterexample.

15. All real numbers are rational numbers.

16. The absolute value of a negative number is always positive.

Simplify each expression.

17. $-\frac{1}{2}(4 - 6a)$

18. $-2(-3 + 2a)$

Write an expression for each phrase.

19. 4 minus the sum of a number and 6

20. 1 more than the quotient of n and 2

Simplify each expression. Justify each step.

21. $\frac{1}{4}(4x - 8) + 3x$

22. $(4^2 - 2^3)(1^3 - 3^2)$

Chapter Test (continued)   Form A

Chapter 1

Simplify each expression.

23. $-4\frac{3}{5} - 2\frac{1}{2}$

24. $6.2 - 9.7 + (-3.1)$

25. Critical Thinking Explain the error in the work shown below. Compute the correct answer.

$$9 + 12 \div 3 = 21 \div 3$$
$$= 7$$

26. Open-Ended Write an expression containing three integers that has a value of zero. One integer should be inside absolute value symbols.

In which quadrant or on which axis would you find each point?

27. $(-1, -3)$

28. $(-2, 0)$

29. Geometry Find the area of a triangle whose vertices have coordinates $(3, 1), (-4, 1),$ and $(3, 5)$.

30. On a diving exercise, a submarine rose 20 ft, dove 40 ft, rose 7 ft, and rose 13 ft. What was the change in depth after the exercise?

31. At 9:00 A.M., the temperature was $-7°F$. By noon, the temperature was $19°F$. What was the change in temperature?

32. A bicycle cost $359.99 plus sales tax at the rate of 6.2%. Find the total cost of the bicycle.

Use the scatter plot below for Exercises 33–34.

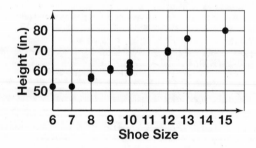

33. Is there a positive correlation, negative correlation, or no correlation between height and shoe size?

34. What is the approximate height of a person with a shoe size of 11?

35. Writing Determine which is greater and explain why.

$\frac{2}{9}, 0.23$

Chapter Test
Chapter 1

Form B

Use an equation to model the relationship in each table.

1.

Number of Items	Total Cost
1	$3.45
2	$6.90
3	$10.35
4	$13.80

2.

Games Played	Games Remaining
10	152
50	112
100	62
162	0

Simplify.

3. $-3 + 8 \div 2 + 7$

4. $-23.8 + 19.4$

5. $-7(2) - (-12)$

6. $-63 \div 9$

Evaluate each expression.

7. $3x - 9$ for $x = 3$

8. $y^2 \div z$ for $y = -14$ and $z = 4$

9. $|m| - |-2n|$ for $m = -11$ and $n = 8$

10. $-2(s - 6t)$ for $s = 2.9$ and $t = -3.8$

11. $\frac{a}{b}$ for $a = -\frac{3}{4}$ and $b = \frac{7}{8}$

12. $\frac{4 + 2d}{-2}$ for $d = -7$

Find the sum or difference.

13. $\begin{bmatrix} -2 & 13 \\ 8 & -6 \end{bmatrix} - \begin{bmatrix} 8 & -17 \\ -8 & -4 \end{bmatrix}$

14. $\begin{bmatrix} 1.2 & -6.8 \\ 0.4 & 0 \\ 2.3 & -8 \end{bmatrix} + \begin{bmatrix} 2.5 & 3.6 \\ -2.7 & -0.1 \\ 2.4 & -7.3 \end{bmatrix}$

Is each statement *true* or *false*? If the statement is false, give a counterexample.

15. All rational numbers are real numbers.

16. The opposite of the absolute value of a positive number is positive.

Simplify each expression.

17. $(18 - 36b)\left(-\frac{2}{3}\right)$

18. $-\frac{1}{4}(12 - 4b)$

Write an expression for each phrase.

19. 5 more than the product of 4 and m

20. the sum of a number and 5 times the difference of 6 and the number

Simplify each expression. Justify each step.

21. $-7x + \frac{1}{4}(4x - 4)$

22. $(2^3 - 3^2)(4^2 - 4^3)$

Chapter Test (continued)   Form B

Chapter 1

Simplify each expression.

23. $-6\frac{2}{3} - 5\frac{2}{3}$ **24.** $-4.7 - 2.3 - 3.8$

25. Critical Thinking Explain the error in the work shown below. Compute the correct answer.

$$5 + 4 \times 3 = 9 \times 3$$
$$= 27$$

26. Open-Ended Choose five different integers so that the average will be −11.

In which quadrant or on which axis would you find each point?

27. $(0, 3)$ **28.** $(-2, 2)$

29. Geometry Find the area of the rectangle whose vertices have coordinates $(-2, -2), (3, -2), (3, 4)$ and $(-2, 4)$.

30. A checking account had the following activity over a 2-day period: a withdrawal of $35.47, a deposit of $92.63, and a service charge of $2.13. If the balance after this activity was $174.13, what was the balance before the activity?

31. A football team begins a possession on its own 27-yard line. Four plays result in the following: gain of 6, loss of 12, gain of 2, loss of 7. On what yard line is the ball after the fourth play?

32. A stereo cost $479.69 plus state and local taxes totaling 7.2%. Find the total cost of the stereo.

Use the scatter plot below for Exercises 33–34.

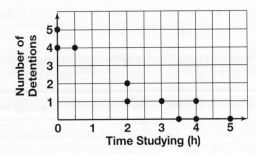

33. Is there a positive correlation, negative correlation, or no correlation between hours spent studying and the number of school detentions received?

34. What is the approximate number of hours spent studying by someone who has received 3 detentions?

35. Writing Determine which is the lesser quantity and explain why it is less.

$$-2\frac{5}{11}, \; -2.45$$

Alternative Assessment

Chapter 1

Form C

TASK 1

In each sentence below, circle the key words or phrases that indicate a mathematical operation and write the symbol for the operation above the words or phrases. Write an equation for each sentence.

a. A number multiplied by 8 and divided by four gives 7 more than the number.

b. Five times a number decreased by eight is equal to thirty-two.

c. The sum of the square of a number and a second number is forty-two.

d. One-third of a number added to itself equals three times the difference of the number and seven.

TASK 2

Two students write the following expressions to answer an exercise:

$$7 + 4(5 - 3)^2 + \frac{9}{3} \quad \text{and} \quad \frac{9}{3} + (5 - 3)^2 \cdot 4 + 7.$$

a. Simplify the two expressions. List each step you use.

b. Explain the similarities in the steps.

c. Make up another expression that uses the same numbers and operations but has a different answer. Then simplify the expression, listing each step.

TASK 3

a. A friend asks you for help with adding, subtracting, multiplying, and dividing positive and negative integers. Using your own words, write rules for each operation: addition, subtraction, multiplication, and division. Make up two examples that demonstrate how each rule works.

b. The same friend is having trouble comparing rational numbers. Write an explanation that will tell your friend how to decide if a rational number is greater than, less than, or equal to another rational number.

c. Add the two matrices below. Then subtract the second matrix from the first.

$$\begin{bmatrix} -2 & 5.1 \\ 1.4 & -3 \end{bmatrix}, \begin{bmatrix} 4 & -6.1 \\ 0 & -3.2 \end{bmatrix}$$

TASK 4

You plan to buy a car that costs $12,000. You have saved $2,000 to use as a down payment towards the purchase. Two different banks have agreed to give you a loan for the car with the following terms:

Bank A offers you a $10,000 loan at a 9% interest rate for four years.

Bank B offers you a $10,000 loan at an 8% interest rate for five years.

a. Explain which loan you will choose and why. You may use the equation $I = prt$, where I is the total interest paid, p is the amount borrowed, r is the interest rate, and t is the number of years.

b. How much money will you save by selecting the loan you have chosen?

Cumulative Review
•••
Chapter 1

For Exercises 1–12, choose the correct letter.

1. The total cost for fair tickets for a family equals the number of adults at $4.00 each plus the number of children at $2.00 each. Which equation could be used to model this situation?

   A. $T = 4a + 2c$ **B.** $C = 2a + 4c$ **C.** $T = 4a + c$ **D.** $T = 4(a + 2c)$

2. Simplify $18 + 3(16 \div 8) \cdot 5$.

   A. 21   **B.** 48   **C.** 120   **D.** 210

3. The opposite of -15 is which of the following?

   A. 15   **B.** 51   **C.** $-\frac{1}{15}$ **D.** $\frac{1}{15}$

4. Simplify $(-2)^3$.

   A. 8   **B.** 6   **C.** -6 **D.** -8

5. Simplify $4(-3)^2 + 6$.

   A. 22   **B.** 42   **C.** 144   **D.** -3

6. Which of the following is equivalent to $x \cdot \frac{1}{y}$?

   A. $\frac{1}{x}$ **B.** $\frac{y}{x}$ **C.** $\frac{x}{y}$ **D.** $y - \frac{1}{x}$

7. Which of the following is true?

   A. $\frac{1}{5} < \frac{1}{6}$ **B.** $-\frac{1}{5} > \frac{1}{6}$ **C.** $-\frac{1}{6} < -\frac{1}{8}$ **D.** $\frac{1}{6} < -\frac{1}{8}$

8. Evaluate $3(x^3 - 5x) + 6$ for $x = 3$.

   A. 0   **B.** 36   **C.** 42   **D.** 87

9. Evaluate $\frac{2(x^2 + 18)}{x}$ for $x = 4$.

   A. 17   **B.** 11   **C.** 8.5   **D.** 68

10. Simplify $|18.4 - 32.1|$.

    A. 13.7   **B.** -13.7 **C.** 23.3   **D.** 4.3

11. Which of the following is a rational number?

    A. π **B.** $\sqrt{7}$ **C.** $\sqrt{\frac{20}{10}}$ **D.** $0.666666\ldots$

12. Evaluate $|p| - |3q|$ for $p = -2$ and $q = 3$.

    A. -11 **B.** 7   **C.** -7 **D.** 11

Cumulative Review (continued)

Chapter 1

For Exercises 13–16, compute the answer.

13. Evaluate $\dfrac{x^4}{x + 6}$ for $x = 3$.

14. Simplify $-23 - (-32)$.

15. Evaluate $6xy + \dfrac{-x}{4}$ for $x = 4$ and $y = 3$.

16. Evaluate $|3d + 4|$ for $d = -9$.

Use an equation to model the relationship in each table.

17.

Number of Items	Total Cost
1	$1.50
2	$3.00
3	$4.50

18.

Hours Worked	Hours Remaining
1.5 h	6.5 h
3 h	5 h
4.5 h	3.5 h

Find the sum or difference.

19. $\begin{bmatrix} 6.7 & -2.6 \\ 3.5 & -1.7 \end{bmatrix} + \begin{bmatrix} -3.3 & 2.9 \\ -0.2 & 1.1 \end{bmatrix}$

20. $\begin{bmatrix} 6 & 5 \\ -7 & 1 \\ -3 & 8 \end{bmatrix} - \begin{bmatrix} -5 & 2 \\ -8 & 1 \\ 4 & -6 \end{bmatrix}$

21. Open-Ended Write 5 different numbers that together have an average of -12. Explain how to find the average of the 5 numbers.

22. Writing Explain the error in the work shown below. Give the correct answer.

$$4 + 3(x - 7) = 7(x - 7)$$
$$= 7x - 49$$

Chapter 1 Answers

Practice 1-1
1. $7 + x$ **2.** $3p$ **3.** $10 - m$ **4.** $7 - n$
5. $2q$ **6.** $m + 3$ **7.** 8 divided by a **8.** 10 less than s
9. 13 more than x **10.** 2 more than the product of a and b

11. $8 - n$ **12.** $4 + n$ **13.** $2n$ **14.** $3 + n$ **15.** $10 + \frac{15}{n}$

16. $n - 12$ **17.** $c = 24.95s$ **18.** $g = 30t$ **19.** $m = 0.10d$
20. $n = 48 - g$ **21.** $c = 8p$ **22.** $c = 32.95p$
23. $c = 3.50t$ **24.** $d = 55h$ **25.** $p = 5h$ **26.** $a = 10 - c$
27. $l = 0.45d$ **28.** $r = 500 - t$

Practice 1-2
1. 52 **2.** 2 **3.** 38 **4.** 4 **5.** 18.9 **6.** 87 **7.** 25 **8.** 7 **9.** 2
10. 1 **11.** 9 **12.** 30.4 **13.** 19 **14.** 5 **15.** 2 **16.** 6 **17.** 26
18. 29 **19.** 31 **20.** 88 **21.** 14.18 **22.** 85 **23.** 28 **24.** 12
25. 26 **26.** 5 **27.** 55 **28.** 56 **29.** 72 **30.** 60 **31.** 40 **32.** 2
33. 11 **34.** 4 **35.** 131 **36.** 141 **37.** 33 **38.** 16 **39.** 22
40. 12 **41.** 2 **42.** 1 **43.** 56 **44.** \$33.95 **45.** \$63.34 **46.** 24
47. 2.25 **48.** 0 **49.** 99 **50.** 5 **51.** 6

Practice 1-3
1. rational, real **2.** rational, real **3.** natural, whole, integers, rational, real **4.** irrational, real **5.** irrational, real
6. integers, rational, real **7.** rational, real **8.** natural, whole, integers, rational, real **9.** true **10.** false; -2 **11.** true
12. false; $7 \times 2 = 14$ **13.** > **14.** < **15.** < **16.** = **17.** >

18. < **19.** $-\frac{8}{9}, -\frac{22}{25}, -\frac{7}{8}$ **20.** $-3\frac{12}{25}, -3.45, -3\frac{4}{9}$

21. $-\frac{1}{3}, -\frac{1}{4}, -\frac{1}{5}$ **22.** $-1\frac{7}{9}, -1\frac{3}{4}, -1.7$ **23.** $-\frac{7}{8}, -\frac{3}{4}, -\frac{2}{3}$

24. $2\frac{5}{8}, 2.7, 2\frac{3}{4}$ **25.** whole **26.** rational **27.** whole

28. irrational **29.** $\frac{3}{10}$ **30.** 327 **31.** 3.46 **32.** $\frac{1}{2}$

33. \$154.23, 0.0375, $\frac{30}{365}$, \$.48, 0.055, and $3\frac{1}{2}$ are rational

and real; \$8000 and \$1540 are whole, integers, rational, and real.

Practice 1-4
1. 2 **2.** -15 **3.** -14 **4.** -17 **5.** -41 **6.** 5 **7.** 19.7

8. -16.2 **9.** -7.6 **10.** $-\frac{1}{2}$ **11.** $\frac{1}{3}$ **12.** $-\frac{5}{12}$ **13.** $1\frac{2}{3}$

14. $-2\frac{1}{4}$ **15.** $-2\frac{1}{3}$ **16.** 1.9 **17.** -0.99 **18.** 1.2 **19.** 33

20. 7 **21.** -7 **22.** -0.9 **23.** -0.7 **24.** -5 **25.** 5

26. -18 **27.** 1 **28.** -6 **29.** $\frac{5}{12}$ **30.** $-2\frac{1}{3}$

31. $\begin{bmatrix} 3 & 1 \\ 0 & 2 \end{bmatrix}$ **32.** $\begin{bmatrix} 0.4 \\ -0.4 \\ 1.1 \end{bmatrix}$

33. $-18°$F **34.** their own 11-yd line **35.** \$170.53 **36.** -39 ft

Practice 1-5
1. 7 **2.** -16 **3.** -12 **4.** -8 **5.** 43 **6.** -49 **7.** -21.4

8. 14.6 **9.** -9 **10.** 26.4 **11.** 12 **12.** -10.6 **13.** $-\frac{1}{2}$

14. -1 **15.** $\frac{1}{2}$ **16.** -18 **17.** 12 **18.** -5.9 **19.** 24 **20.** 10.5

21. -0.99 **22.** 3 **23.** 9 **24.** -3 **25.** 9 **26.** -3 **27.** 3
28. 17 **29.** -8 **30.** -19 **31.** -7 **32.** -7 **33.** -8
34. $\begin{bmatrix} -8 & 1 \\ 5 & -4 \end{bmatrix}$ **35.** $\begin{bmatrix} -0.9 & -1.7 \\ -2.1 & -6.3 \end{bmatrix}$
36. $29°$F **37.** 29,310 ft
38. $-$\$205.72 **39.** their own 35-yd line

Practice 1-6
1. -16 **2.** 54 **3.** 81 **4.** -32 **5.** -48 **6.** 196 **7.** 48 **8.** 6
9. 4 **10.** 120 **11.** -49 **12.** -243 **13.** -4 **14.** -2 **15.** 15

16. -125 **17.** 4 **18.** 112 **19.** $-\frac{4}{5}$ **20.** -32 **21.** 49

22. -200 **23.** -20 **24.** 256 **25.** -11 **26.** 32 **27.** 0

28. -4 **29.** $-\frac{7}{4}$ **30.** 16 **31.** 2 **32.** 91 **33.** 64 **34.** -120

35. -7 **36.** 3 **37.** 64 **38.** -15 **39.** -5 **40.** -15 **41.** 4
42. 72 **43.** -27 **44.** -1019 **45.** -15 **46.** -4 **47.** 108
48. 256

Practice 1-7
1. $2x + 12$ **2.** $-40 + 5b$ **3.** $-4x + 28$ **4.** $-15c + 21$

5. $-7.5a - 12.5$ **6.** $-3k + 12$ **7.** $-9 + 12d$ **8.** $4h - \frac{2}{3}$

9. $19.2x - 12.6$ **10.** $10.5x - 28$ **11.** $4x + 28$
12. $-5a + 10$ **13.** $8 - 10d$ **14.** $-2k + 22$ **15.** $-2h - 5$
16. $-8c + 32$ **17.** $-4 + 2b$ **18.** $6x - 18$ **19.** $8r + 32$
20. $-5b + 25$ **21.** $3f + 6$ **22.** $11h - 25$ **23.** $d - 21$
24. $1 + 8x$ **25.** $2h + 4$ **26.** $8 + 2y$ **27.** $-n - 2$
28. $3w + 12$ **29.** $1.2d - 2$ **30.** $-2d + 6$ **31.** $5x + 12$
32. $6a + 4$ **33.** $3t - 15$ **34.** $-b + 20$ **35.** $2k + 6$
36. $0.8s + 1.6$ **37.** $6b - 18$ **38.** $6n - 4$ **39.** $x - 2$

40. $2a + 7$ **41.** $9 + 10c$ **42.** $1 + \frac{2}{5}a$ **43.** $15x + 60$

44. $2m + 2$ **45.** $8a - 9$ **46.** $2x - 15$ **47.** $3t - 36$
48. $-18 - 6k$ **49.** $5(x + 6)$ **50.** $2(y - 8)$

51. $-15(x - 5)$ **52.** $\frac{32}{y + 12}$ **53.** $-8(4 - w)$

54. $(x + 9)(7 - x)$

Chapter 1 Answers (continued)

Practice 1-8

1. Comm. Prop. of Add. **2.** Comm. Prop. of Add.
3. Ident. Prop. of Mult. **4.** Distributive Prop.
5. Assoc. Prop. of Mult. **6.** Inverse Prop. of Mult.
7. Distributive Prop. **8.** Comm. Prop. of Add.
9. Assoc. Prop. of Add. **10.** Inverse Prop. of Add.
11. Comm. Prop. of Add. **12.** Assoc. Prop. of Mult.
13. Ident. Prop. of Add. **14.** Comm. Prop. of Add.
15. Distributive Prop. **16.** Mult. Prop. of Zero
17. Assoc. Prop. of Add. **18.** Comm. Prop. of Mult.
19. Comm. Prop. of Mult. **20.** Comm. Prop. of Add.
21a. Distributive Prop. **21b.** Comm. Prop. of Add.
21c. Assoc. Prop. of Add. **21d.** Distributive Prop.
21e. addition **22a.** Distributive Prop. **22b.** def. of subtr.
22c. Comm. Prop. of Add. **22d.** Distributive Prop.
22e. addition **22f.** def. of subtr. **23a.** Distributive Prop.
23b. Comm. Prop. of Add. **23c.** Distributive Prop.
23d. addition **24.** 80 **25.** 7200 **26.** 2400 **27.** 18
28. $7 **29.** $28 **30.** $16

Practice 1-9

1. $(-5, 4)$ **2.** $(6, 2)$ **3.** $(1, -3)$ **4.** $(-6, -5)$
5. II **6.** III **7.** I **8.** IV
9.

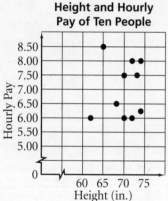

Height and Hourly Pay of Ten People

10.

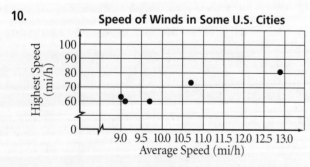

Speed of Winds in Some U.S. Cities

11. no correlation **12.** positive correlation **13.** no correlation; a person's age is not related to the number of pets he/she may have. **14.** negative correlation; the more times you brush, the fewer the cavities you are likely to have. **15.** positive correlation; the more rainy days, the more umbrellas are likely to be sold. **16.** positive correlation
17. negative correlation **18.** no correlation

Reteaching 1-1

1. $n + 5$ **2.** $n - 8$ **3.** $\frac{n}{9}$ **4.** $5n - 3$ **5.** $12n = 84$

6. $n - 7 = 22$ **7.** $8x = 72$ **8.** $\frac{n}{3} = 18$

Reteaching 1-2

1. Check students' work. **2.** Check students' work.
3. Check students' work. **4.** Check students' work.
5. -3 **6.** -75 **7.** 2 **8.** 28 **9.** 3 **10.** -1
11. -20 **12.** -56

Reteaching 1-3

1. rational, real **2.** rational, real **3.** whole, integer, rational, real **4.** rational, real **5.** irrational, real **6.** integers, rational, real **7.** rational, real **8.** natural, whole, integers, rational, real **9.** natural, whole, integers, rational, real **10.** integers, rational, real **11.** rational, real **12.** irrational, real
13.–18. Check students' work.

Reteaching 1-4

1. -7 **2.** 17 **3.** 3 **4.** -10 **5.** -5 **6.** -3 **7.** 2 **8.** -1
9. -3.8 **10.** 7.6 **11.** -2.3 **12.** 21.2 **13.** 0.2 **14.** -10.3
15. -20 **16.** -6.3 **17.** -1 **18.** -9 **19.** 1 **20.** 9
21. 5.9 **22.** 0.9 **23.** -0.9 **24.** -5.9 **25.** 10.5 **26.** 3.7
27. -3.7 **28.** -10.5

Reteaching 1-5

1. -5 **2.** -3 **3.** 9 **4.** 10 **5.** -10 **6.** -9 **7.** -1 **8.** 7
9. 2.3 **10.** 3.2 **11.** -14.4 **12.** -7.3 **13.** 6.2 **14.** -1.6
15. -1.2 **16.** -13.7 **17.** -7 **18.** 1 **19.** -1 **20.** 7 **21.** 13

22. -3 **23.** 7 **24.** -5 **25.** $\begin{bmatrix} -6 & -3 \\ -2 & -3 \end{bmatrix}$ **26.** $\begin{bmatrix} -\frac{1}{6} \\ 2 \end{bmatrix}$

Reteaching 1-6

1.–8. Check students' work. **9.** -8 **10.** -72 **11.** 10
12. -88 **13.** 49 **14.** 50

Reteaching 1-7

1. $10x + 8$ **2.** $3x - 2$ **3.** $28x - 12$ **4.** $20 + 10x$
5. $30 - 18x$ **6.** $3x - 5$ **7.** $6x - 12$ **8.** $21x + 28$
9. $8x + 8y$ **10.** $-4x - 3$ **11.** $2x - 1$ **12.** $6x + 3$
13. $-14x + 3$ **14.** $7x + 1$ **15.** $-3x - 4$

Reteaching 1-8

1. Assoc. Prop. of Add. **2.** Distributive Prop.
3. Comm. Prop. of Mult. **4.** Assoc. Prop. of Mult.
5. Distributive Prop. **6.** Comm. Prop. of Add. **7.** 12 **8.** 8
9. 9; 9 **10.** 8 **11.** 6 **12.** 7; 7

Chapter 1 Answers (continued)

Reteaching 1-9

1. $(-8, 4)$ **2.** $(-4, 0)$ **3.** $(-2, 2)$ **4.** $(0, 3)$ **5.** $(2, 1)$
6. $(7, 4)$ **7.** $(8, -3)$ **8.** $(5, -6)$ **9.** $(-3, -5)$ **10.** $(-6, -8)$
11.–16.

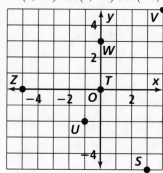

Enrichment 1-1

1. $O = 2I + 1$ **2.** $O = 3I - 1$ **3.** $O = I^2 - 1$

4. $S = 16T^2$ **5.** $R = \frac{3}{4}T + 7$ **6.** $P = 2^E + 1$

7. Check students' work.

Enrichment 1-2

Answers may vary. Samples include:

1. $3 \times 2 \times 2$ **2.** $\sqrt{(8 + 8)}$ **3.** 2^3 **4.** $(3 + 7) \times 4$
5. $(3 + 6) \div 3$ **6.** $30 \div 6 \times 5$ **7.** $(3 \times 9) - 2$ **8.** $4 + 3^2$
9. $(10 \div 2) + (3 \times 3)$ **10.** $\sqrt{25} \times 3 - 2 - 1$
11. $(5 + 3 - 4) \times 3$ **12.** $3 \times (8 - 2)$
13. $(4 \times 4) + (2 \times 4) - 6$

Enrichment 1-3

Check students' work.

Enrichment 1-4

Answers may vary. Samples include:
1. Check students' work. **2.** 6 black and 2 red or 4 black
3. 7 black and 1 red or 6 black **4.** 1 black and 5 red or 4 red
5. 2 black and 3 red or 1 red **6.** 12; 12 black **7.** -5; 5 red
8. -15; 15 red **9.** 11; 11 black **10.** 11; 11 black
11. 2; 2 black

Enrichment 1-5

Check students' work.

Enrichment 1-6

1. 720 **2.** 120 **3.** 17,280 **4.** 6 **5.** 20 **6.** 6 **7.** 120 **8.** 120
9. 625

Enrichment 1-7

1. yes **2.** yes **3.** You always get the final answer of 2.
4. You always get 10 times your original number.

5. For Exercise 3:

x
$x + 5$
$4(x + 5) = 4x + 20$
$4x + 8$
$x + 2$
2

For Exercise 4:

x
$10x$
$10x + 5$
$2(10x + 5) = 20x + 10$
$20x$
$10x$

Enrichment 1-8

1. 4 **2.** 4 **3.** 2 **4.** 0 **5.** 5 **6.** 3 **7.** 6 **8.** 1
9. $1 \times 6 = 6 \times 1 = 6$; $1 \times 5 = 5 \times 1 = 5$;
$1 \times 4 = 4 \times 1 = 4$; $1 \times 3 = 3 \times 1 = 3$; and so on.
10. 1 and 1; 2 and 4; 3 and 5; 4 and 2; 5 and 3; 6 and 6; 0 has no
multiplicative inverse. **11.** 3 **12.** 4 **13.** 0 **14.** 0 **15.** 0
16. 5 **17.** 4 **18.** 2 **19.** 4 **20.** 1

Enrichment 1-9

1.–5.

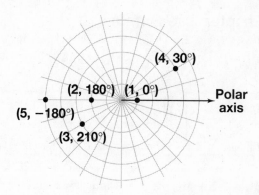

6.–10.

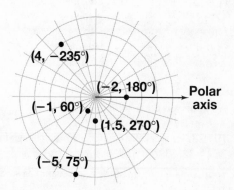

Chapter Project

Activity 1: Researching
Check students' work.

Activity 2: Analyzing
Check students' work.

Activity 3: Organizing
Check students' work.

Activity 4: Calculating
Check students' work.

Chapter 1 Answers (continued)

✔ Checkpoint Quiz 1

1. $14 + x; 18$ **2.** $5z; 7$ **3.** $x + y; 1$ **4.** $\frac{24}{x}; 6$
5. $4z; 5.6$ **6.** $(y + z) + 10; 8.4$ **7.** $y + 2x; 5$ **8.** $xz; 5.6$
9. false; Answers may vary. Sample: The opposite of the opposite of -2 is -2 which is not a positive number.
10. false; Answers may vary. Sample: $-5°F$ is a reasonable temperature but is not a whole number.

✔ Checkpoint Quiz 2

1. $5w + 11$ **2.** 216 **3.** 100 **4.** 45 **5.** $-21 - 8w$

6. $6 + 5x$ **7.** 2.9 **8.** $-2\frac{1}{2}$ **9.** $-6x + 2y$

10a.
$4w + 7w + 21$	Distributive Prop.
$(4w + 7w) + 21$	Assoc. Prop. of Add.
$(4 + 7)w + 21$	Distributive Prop.
$11w + 21$	Addition

10b. -23

Chapter Test, Form A

1. $s = 150m$ **2.** $r = 100 - t$ **3.** 20 **4.** 15 **5.** 16 **6.** -32

7. 29 **8.** -16 **9.** 8 **10.** 32.2 **11.** $-\frac{4}{5}$ **12.** -3

13. $\begin{bmatrix} 6 & -4 \\ 0 & -10 \end{bmatrix}$ **14.** $\begin{bmatrix} -1.3 & -10.4 \\ 3.1 & 0.1 \\ -0.1 & -0.7 \end{bmatrix}$

15. false; $\sqrt{2}$ is a real number that is not rational. **16.** true
17. $-2 + 3a$ **18.** $6 - 4a$ **19.** $4 - (x + 6)$ **20.** $\frac{n}{2} + 1$

21.
$x - 2 + 3x$	Distributive Prop.
$x + 3x - 2$	Comm. Prop. of Add.
$(1 + 3)x - 2$	Distributive Prop.
$4x - 2$	Addition

22.
$(16 - 8)(1 - 9)$	Exponents
$(8)(-8)$	Subtraction
-64	Multiplication

23. $-7\frac{1}{10}$ **24.** -6.6
25. Addition was done before division; 13
26. Answers may vary. Sample: $|-7| - 4 - 3$
27. III **28.** x-axis **29.** 14 units^2 **30.** no change in depth
31. $26°F$ **32.** 382.31 **33.** positive correlation
34. approximately 65 in. **35.** $\frac{2}{9}$ is less than 0.23 since $\frac{2}{9} = 0.\overline{2}$ and $0.\overline{2} < 0.23$.

Chapter Test, Form B

1. $c = 3.45n$ **2.** $r = 162 - p$ **3.** 8 **4.** -4.4 **5.** -2 **6.** -7

7. 0 **8.** 49 **9.** -5 **10.** -51.4 **11.** $-\frac{6}{7}$ **12.** 5

13. $\begin{bmatrix} -10 & 30 \\ 16 & -2 \end{bmatrix}$ **14.** $\begin{bmatrix} 3.7 & -3.2 \\ -2.3 & -0.1 \\ 4.7 & -15.3 \end{bmatrix}$

15. true **16.** false; Answers may vary. Sample: The opposite of $|7|$ is -7 which is not positive. **17.** $-12 + 24b$

18. $-3 + b$ **19.** $4m + 5$ **20.** $x + 5(6 - x)$
21.
$-7x + x - 1$	Distributive Prop.
$(-7 + 1)x - 1$	Distributive Prop.
$-6x - 1$	Addition

22.
$(8 - 9)(16 - 64)$	Exponents
$(-1)(-48)$	Subtraction
48	Multiplication

23. $-12\frac{1}{3}$ **24.** -10.8
25. Addition was done before multiplication; 17
26. Answers may vary. Sample: $-7, -36, 14, -15,$ and -11
27. y-axis **28.** II **29.** 30 units^2 **30.** 119.10
31. on the team's 16-yd line **32.** 514.23
33. negative correlation **34.** one h

35. $-2\frac{5}{11}$ is less than -2.45 since $-2\frac{5}{11} = -2.\overline{45}$ and $-2.\overline{45} < -2.45$.

Alternative Assessment, Form C

TASK 1 Scoring Guide:

a. $\frac{8x}{4} = 7 + x$ **b.** $5x - 8 = 32$

c. $x^2 + y = 42$ **d.** $\frac{1}{3}x + x = 3(x - 7)$

3 Shows a clear understanding of the concepts of translating words to mathematical equations and can identify the key words or phrases. The sentences are all written correctly.

2 Translations are given for each of the exercises with minor errors.

1 Student makes some attempt to write the translations. The equations are translated incorrectly.

0 No attempt is made, or no solution is presented.

TASK 2 Scoring Guide:

a. 26

b. In either case, the same order of operations must be followed.

c. Check students' work.

3 Both expressions are correctly simplified. Each step is clearly identified and explained. The steps are compared, and explanations show a thorough understanding of grouping symbols, exponents, and order of operations. A new expression is presented and simplified correctly.

2 The answer is mostly correct, but some steps are omitted. A clear explanation is given, but it shows a lesser degree of insight.

1 The response is partially satisfactory, but major steps are omitted. Explanations are incomplete or unclear.

0 No attempt is made, or no solution is presented.

Chapter 1 Answers (continued)

TASK 3 Scoring Guide:

a. Check students' work.

b. Check students' work.

c. Sum is $\begin{bmatrix} 2 & -1 \\ 1.4 & -6.2 \end{bmatrix}$; difference is $\begin{bmatrix} -6 & 11.2 \\ 1.4 & 0.2 \end{bmatrix}$

3 Clear and coherent rules are given. These show a thorough, in-depth understanding of operations using negative integers and rational numbers. Examples are appropriately chosen and clearly support the student's rules. The sum and difference of the two matrices are correctly calculated.

2 Rules are given for most of the operations, with one or two operations omitted or unclear. Examples and matrix calculations are essentially correct, but may contain minor computational errors.

1 Student makes some attempt to write rules and to find the sum and difference of the matrices. Example are omitted. Matrix operations are not well understood.

0 No attempt is made, or no solution is presented.

TASK 4 Scoring Guide:

a. Bank A since the total amount of interest to be repaid is $3600 compared to $4000 with Bank B.

b. $400

3 For each loan, interest calculations are correctly computed and the total amount paid out over time is shown. Regardless of the loan selected, a clear and well-organized rationale is presented in favor of one loan over the other. The equation is correct and the variables are identified.

2 There are minor computational errors, but reasoning in support of the loan selection is sound. The equation is correct but the variables are not identified.

1 There are major computational errors, and the loan selection is not well supported. The equation is incorrect and the variables are not identified.

0 No attempt is made, or no solution is presented.

Cumulative Review

1. A **2.** B **3.** A **4.** D **5.** B **6.** C **7.** C **8.** C **9.** A **10.** A
11. D **12.** C **13.** 9 **14.** 9 **15.** 71 **16.** 23 **17.** $c = 1.5n$
18. $r = 8 - w$

19. $\begin{bmatrix} 3.4 & 0.3 \\ 3.3 & -0.6 \end{bmatrix}$ **20.** $\begin{bmatrix} 11 & 3 \\ 1 & 0 \\ -7 & 14 \end{bmatrix}$

21. Answers may vary. Sample: $30, -17, -80, 15, -8$; To find the average of the five numbers, add them and divide by 5.
22. Addition was done before multiplication (distribution); $3x - 17$